SONATA in A major, Op.2 No.2

Allegro Vivace

Beware of taking this movement too fast. The direction *vivace* describes the energy of the music, but the notation in crochets and quavers does not mean any such tempo as would make the triplet semiquavers unintelligible. Take your tempo from these, aiming at great brilliance and a big tone from the full height of the finger-fall. Even in bb.1 & 3, which are *piano*, the demisemiquaver in both hands should bristle with energy. The temptation to a dangerous tempo results from the tremolo bass of bb.58–75. The student should realise betimes that the tremolo, like its special case the trill, depends for its effect much more upon equality of tone and time than upon rapidity, and that it is at its best when the player is playing a definite number of notes. Here in bb.58–75 you will find that if you have always kept your notes even and regulated your *crescendo* note by note, the bass begins to sound continuous and dramatic at a pace you might have thought childishly cautious. The incidental details off the beat at each upward step, if mastered from the outset with the rest of the passage, greatly enhance its dramatic tone-colour. Players, young and old, too often despise such opportunities for developing a good rhythmically regular tremolo.

Bars 84 ff. The triplet octaves are characteristic of Beethoven's early pianoforte style. They are suited to a large hand, to which they are not much more difficult than 6ths. The fingering is Beethoven's own. If two hands are used (as here suggested), the player should avoid accentuating the l.h., and should accordingly use it at the ends of the rising triplets instead of at the beginning as in descending. The touch should, in short, be such as would be natural if the passage ran as follows:

Accordingly it is a mistake to attempt Beethoven's fingering if the hand is too small for a tolerable legato. But it is a worse mistake to give hard accents to the l.h.

b.104 Some editions published in Beethoven's lifetime add an upper minim E, corresponding to that in b.108 and to the A in the parallel passage at b.324. The parallel passage is no evidence, as the A is there necessary on other grounds. We are not obliged to assume that Beethoven noticed or consented to the E in b.104, and the entry of the minims is much better without it. According to one account it was the head of the *p* which happened to light upon the bottom line of the stave.

b.117 Beethoven marks both parts of this movement to be repeated. According to Mandyczewski, Beethoven intended to repeat the second part from b.121/2; and also to have a 2-bar silence at b.117, which is not very convincing. In public performance this highly dramatic movement is more impressive without repeats at all.

bb.181 ff. It shows the moderation of Beethoven's demands on other players, that though his early favourite broken-octave device shows that he could easily stretch

10ths, he never writes suc[...] even under the temptation of such poly[...] here. The 'grace-notes' (a misnomer in this case) must have as much tone as the rest of the inner part which they represent, and must, of course, fall on the time as represented by the bass. The delay in the treble will not be noticed; whereas if the 'grace-notes' come before their time they will not be heard. Players with very large hands may take the 10th according to the sense – viz.:

Note that Beethoven *does* expect the player to stretch a 9th. The bracketed *tenuto* mark is not his; but he writes a crochet at the top and puts no staccato sign upon it. His intention is unmistakable.

Largo Appassionato

Bars 1–8 The technical task of the staccato bass cannot fail to fascinate the student. The chords above, l.h. included, must be religiously sustained, without gaps even between repeated notes. Learn betimes the beauty of their sound as reverberating *only* by contrast with the staccato bass, which does actually reinforce with its own harmonics each tonic chord like a very ethereal pedal. The gross mechanism of the ordinary pedal is therefore forbidden here. It must be reserved for the climax. It is not wanted even if you cannot stretch the 10th in b.3. On no account play that bass-note before the beat; put it exactly together with the right hand, and nobody will even suspect that the E has been delayed.

In the 3rd crotchet of b.3 there is no means of indicating that the D belongs to the staccato part as well as to the chord. Strange to say, its disappearance from the staccato part will not be missed unless you have been indiscreet enough to put a swell there. On the other hand, it absolutely must be held as a note of the chord.

bb.17–18 Much more difficult than any detail of this delightful task is the climax at bb.17–18. Before you attempt anything else in this movement, find out what your biggest tone amounts to in those bars, taking care that the melody dominates in every chord. With careful pedalling you may lift your hands without breaking the legato. Remember that a thunderous bass is worse than useless unless the treble (*not* a few chance inner notes) can dominate.

Having ascertained what you can do properly here, be contented with it and grade your *crescendo* up to it and not beyond. Your tone will grow if (and only if) you do not ruin your ear by letting it get used to ill-balanced chords and ugly qualities.

bb.9–13, 40–43 Beethoven's different beginnings to the trill show his sensitiveness to harmonic colour according to whether the melody is in the treble or the bass. The plain trill cannot follow the old rule of beginning with the upper note, for that has just been played. The grace-notes, on the other hand, are written in accordance with the old rule; *i.e.,* you are to play –

and no such hiccough as –

Scherzo

The semiquaver figure is very difficult, especially in the left hand, where you had certainly better 'change feet' on the middle step , as you may find easier to do in the right hand. Do not begin by trying to make it glitter; the glitter will come from inveterate accuracy in slow practice with attention to the precise (and *minimum*) movement of the hand. An 'agogic accent' (which the brutal truth calls a drag) on the first note is detestable. On the other hand, do not flick off the crotchet: let it sing, though the softer the better. Eventually (but not before long practice) the tempo should be quite lively, with no stodginess in b.3. Some passion is then possible in the Trio, where Beethoven's phrasing ($1 + 1 + 1 + 1 + 4$) should be respected and the first 4 bars treated as a dialogue.

Rondo

The unusual use of *grazioso* merely as a tempo mark almost suffices to suggest the right pace, which is hardly above *andante.* Semiquavers should flow gently. Too slow a tempo would need a jerk forward into a quicker time for the A minor episode. On the other hand, most people are apt to take that kind of episode far too fast; few players without special information have any idea of the weight of Beethoven's staccato *fortissimos.* They belong to the resources in which the early pianoforte sounded formidable because it was obviously displaying its full strength, whereas the modern pianoforte sounds weak in them because it can make much more noise in other ways.

Accordingly the first thing to practise in this movement is bb.56–99, with the inflexible ambition to express every contrast clearly. The rhythms in the left hand need as much energy as the hail-storm in the right. Persons who are accustomed to no loud staccato less heavy than *martellato* octaves should realise that a hail-storm is more sublime than a coal-shoot in use. When you have learnt to command the stinging tone of this episode you will find that you need not take it any faster than will join smoothly on to the deliberate flow of the *grazioso*; and that if the *grazioso* will not join on to your majestic hail-storm it probably will also fail to flow in itself.

After you have mastered this problem you can attend to finer details. In b.1 you learn (for the first time in Beethoven's Sonatas, taken chronologically) that when Beethoven writes an arpeggio or scale in an irregular number of notes (eleven here) he knows exactly how to divide it; and that if you do anything different your result will be dull. Study each variant of this theme accurately according to Beethoven's directions. Every time you think he has brought the wrong note on to the beat or hurried in the middle instead of at the end, or done other things that would never have occurred to you, the result, when you have got it in *tempo*, will have a sparkle that nothing else could give. Of course, all the notes must be there.

The portamento in b.2 is one of those things which violinists and singers are supposed to do well and pianists not at all. As a matter of fact, the pianoforte can suggest the effect (by balance of tone) much better than the violin can realise it across the strings. It is true, and on the whole fortunate, that the pianoforte cannot slither; but nothing in all Chopin or Liszt suits it better than b.2 of this movement played with a swoop of the wrist down to the thumb on G♯, and all in a quiet tone. Persons who hit the top E smartly, as with a thimble, had better leave music and music-lovers in peace.

Bar 100 A little judicious pedal, at regions selected by experience of each individual pianoforte, will give the student timely opportunity to learn how to listen to his own playing as well as to the criticisms of his teacher. Of course, this does not belong to the stage at which the scale is still being mastered as an even series of notes. But after that stage it is as mistaken to remain contented with dryness as to put up with messiness.

bb.159–160 In early works Beethoven often uses the *ff* mark in purely melodic climaxes without percussion. But while you must avoid percussion in such places, you must not ignore this evidence that his early style was to him anything but a placid imitation of Mozartean smoothness. In the present case, though the climax is melodic, it leads straight back to the 'hail-storm'.

b.180 The last 8 bars must not be hustled, and a good indication of the general tempo may be found in the fact that the cross-slurring of these semiquavers will need a little slackening. Obviously the staccato of the following descending scale has nothing of the hail-storm quality about it.

DONALD FRANCIS TOVEY

Beethoven

Sonata
in A major
FOR PIANO
Op. 2 No. 2

Edited by
HAROLD CRAXTON

Annotated by DONALD
FRANCIS TOVEY

The Associated Board of
the Royal Schools of Music

No. 2

Dedicated to Joseph Haydn

SONATA
in A

BEETHOVEN, Op. 2 No. 2

Allegro vivace

A.B. 233

14

Largo appassionato

SCHERZO
Allegretto

Trio

(legato)

Scherzo D.C.

RONDO
Grazioso

Beethoven Piano music

Sonatas — separate editions

1	Sonata in F minor, Op. 2 No. 1	(D008 2)
2	Sonata in A, Op. 2 No. 2	(D009 0)
3	Sonata in C, Op. 2 No. 3	(D010 4)
4	Sonata in E flat, Op. 7	(D011 2)
5	Sonata in C minor, Op. 10 No. 1	(D012 0)
6	Sonata in F, Op. 10 No. 2	(D013 9)
7	Sonata in D, Op. 10 No. 3	(D014 7)
8	Sonata in C minor, Op. 13 'Pathétique'	(D015 5)
9	Sonata in E, Op. 14 No. 1	(D016 3)
10	Sonata in G, Op. 14 No. 2	(D017 1)
11	Sonata in B flat, Op. 22	(D018X)
12	Sonata in A flat, Op. 26	(D019 8)
13	Sonata in E flat, Op. 27 No. 1	(D020 1)
14	Sonata in C sharp minor, Op. 27 No. 2 'Moonlight'	(D021X)
15	Sonata in D, Op. 28 'Pastorale'	(D022 8)
16	Sonata in G, Op. 31 No. 1	(D023 6)
17	Sonata in D minor, Op. 31 No. 2	(D024 4)
18	Sonata in E flat, Op. 31 No. 3	(D025 2)
19	Sonata in G minor, Op. 49 No. 1	(D026 0)
20	Sonata in G, Op. 49 No. 2	(D027 9)
21	Sonata in C, Op. 53 'Waldstein'	(D028 7)
22	Sonata in F, Op. 54	(D029 5)
23	Sonata in F minor, Op. 57 'Appassionata'	(D030 9)
24	Sonata in F sharp, Op. 78	(D031 7)
25	Sonata in G, Op. 79 'Alla Tedesca'	(D032 5)
26	Sonata in E flat, Op. 81a 'Les adieux'	(D033 3)
27	Sonata in E minor, Op. 90	(D034 1)
28	Sonata in A, Op. 101	(D035X)
29	Sonata in B flat, Op. 106 'Hammerklavier'	(D036 8)
30	Sonata in E, Op. 109	(D037 6)
31	Sonata in A flat, Op. 110	(D038 4)
32	Sonata in C minor, Op. 111	(D039 2)

Sonatas — complete editions

VOLUME I Sonatas Nos. 1–11	Paper	(D053 8)
	Cloth	(D056 2)
VOLUME II Sonatas Nos. 12–22	Paper	(D054 6)
	Cloth	(D057 0)
VOLUME III Sonatas Nos. 23–32	Paper	(D055 4)
	Cloth	(D058 9)

Donald Francis Tovey
A Companion to Beethoven's Pianoforte Sonatas
A bar-by-bar analysis of Beethoven's 32 Pianoforte Sonatas Revised Edition (D086 3)

Other works

Andante Favori, WoO 57	(D267 0)
Bagatelles, Op. 33, Op. 119, Op. 126, WoO 52, WoO 53, WoO 54, WoO 56, WoO 59, WoO 60	(D292 1)
Seven Sonatinas, WoO 47/1–3, WoO 51, Anh. 5/1–2, WoO 50	(D255 7)
Twelve Variations on a Russian Dance from 'Das Waldmädchen', WoO 71	(D601 3)

ISBN 1-85472-009-0

9 781854 720092

The Associated Board of
the Royal Schools of Music
(Publishing) Limited

14 Bedford Square
London WC1B 3JG
United Kingdom

www.abrsmpublishing.co.uk